POWERHOUSE
writing

Grades 4-8

Lisa Dettinger

© 2019 PowerHouse Educational Resources
Vertical Press Books

ISBN-13: 978-1-7336998-0-8

Cover Design by Kaylee Winsand
Logo by Urban Root Creative

Printed in the United States of America.

Table of Contents

How to Use This Book

1. Log in to PowerHouseEdu.com for the online videos or purchase the USB flash drive version of this video course.

2. Watch the first video segment and interact with this workbook according to the video.

3. Repeat until videos and workbook assignments are complete.

4. Yes, it's that simple. (You don't need a teacher's guide.)

Notes

- There's an answer key in the back of the workbook.

- There are eight titled lessons. Most of them have a "Part A" and a "Part B." There are 16 total video sessions.

- This course can be completed in a quarter, a trimester, a semester, or a year. You can decide how many days per week to spend on writing and how quickly or slowly you want to move through the course.

- Got burning questions? Go to PowerHouseEdu.com.

Nouns

comedian	pilot	elevator
sister	mayor	Spongebob
canine	soccer player	bathtub
choir	tarantula	Mr. Smith
King George	Earth	pizza
brother	knight	Kermit the Frog
mansion	enemy	jet
Canada	dinosaur	dragon
trombone	hero	tornado
student	Mike	Mt. Everest
linebacker	Walmart	blizzard
notebook	dad	shadow
homework	centipede	stadium
buddy	music	guitar
furnace	buoy	megaphone
gorilla	White House	carnival
toothpaste	concrete	surgeon
brain	grandmother	plastic wrap
biker	moon	America
kitten	carrot	ointment
salsa	worm	lip balm
post office	stop sign	Mr. Schiffler
idea	Superman	compost
snout	chihuahua	cheeseball
amphibian	station wagon	alien

3

Adjectives

colossal	studious	petite
squishy	immense	blissful
violent	puny	disgusting
mammoth	oblong	golden
microscopic	teeny	triumphant
magnificent	gloomy	syrupy
antique	angelic	pungent
stale	handsome	ferocious
snail-paced	creepy	chintzy
luscious	bubbly	congested
decaying	polished	muscular
splendiferous	toothless	stubborn
zesty	exhilarating	ominous
ambitious	hostile	flamboyant
sinister	delightful	enchanting
magenta	hyper	mesmerizing
striped	vicious	ghastly
metallic	towering	putrid
ecstatic	hilarious	euphoric
quarrelsome	speckled	frigid
explosive	whimsical	accessible
sensational	shabby	immortal
witty	stale	omnipotent
radiant	heroic	victorious
adorable	rip-roaring	intergalactic
calm	glamorous	zesty

4

Verbs

sneezes

discards

hurls

shrieks

demolishes

slithers

bulldozes

inflicts

cruises

oozes

spits

bounces

careens

rockets

crumples

gulps

screeches

rejoices

chatters

jitterbugs

swirls

preys

parachutes

envelops

tiptoes

churns

roars

explodes

sneers

chuckles

splatters

limps

zooms

snickers

hisses

frolics

twinkles

belches

waltzes

stumbles

zips

shudders

writhes

gallops

darts

convulses

sails

tumbles

yanks

twitches

tramples

gurgles

giggles

buzzes

whistles

groans

wanders

pounces

surfs

flutters

stampedes

wrangles

ransacks

gushes

snickers

reverberates

squeaks

whimpers

zaps

ingests

wrestles

melts

combusts

disbands

assimilates

crashes

guzzles

adorns

Adverbs

powerfully	gracefully	regularly
angrily	excitedly	recently
cautiously	royally	outside
brilliantly	passionately	somewhere
secretly	slothfully	underground
swiftly	radically	eternally
stupidly	eagerly	regally
violently	joyfully	substantially
surprisingly	accidentally	crazily
thoroughly	speedily	fearfully
nastily	sharply	violently
crazily	suspiciously	convincingly
nervously	everywhere	forward
awkwardly	yesterday	devastatingly
abruptly	soon	impatiently
smoothly	yonder	continually
selfishly	tomorrow	extremely
boldly	later	cowardly
reluctantly	weekly	intelligently
vigorously	here	accurately
sheepishly	upstairs	diligently
wearily	suddenly	hastily
wisely	nowhere	rarely
stiffly	today	emphatically
fiercely	again	practically
majestically	often	matter-of-factly

6

Prepositions

above
across
after
against
around
at
before
behind
beneath
beside
between
beyond
by
down
during
except
for
from
in
inside
into

like
near
of
off
on
out
past
through
throughout
to
toward
under
until
up
with
within
without

beneath the sea
beside myself
inside the jar

through the flames
with Mr. Schiffler
within reason
above her head
across the river
after breakfast
against all odds
around the world
at noon
before the game
behind the wheel
between us
beyond the horizon
by himself
during the night
down the hill
except the red one
for you
from the beginning
in cahoots
into the cave
like the last time
near the volcano
of little consequence
off her rocker
on top of old smokey
out the door
past the finish line
throughout the day
to you
toward the hoop
under my bed
until 9 o'clock
up a creek
without a paddle
over the river

Materials for Lesson 1:

30 index cards

Markers or colored pencils

(red, blue, brown, green, purple, orange)

Lesson 1

Grammar Power

Worm Words

(You can also record your index card words on these pages.)

Nouns (red)

   1. Worm

   2. _____

   3. _____

   4. _____

   5. _____

worm

Adjectives (brown)

   1. Squishy

   2. _____

   3. _____

   4. _____

   5. _____

squishy

Verbs (blue)

   1. Stretches

   2. _____

   3. _____

   4. _____

   5. _____

stretches

Adverbs (green)

1. Desperately
2. _____
3. _____
4. _____
5. _____

desperately

Determiners/Articles (purple)

1. The
2. A (Use before a word that begins with a consonant.)
3. An (Use before a word that begins with a vowel.)

The

Prepositional Phrases (orange)

1. Toward the edge
2. _____
3. _____
4. _____
5. _____

toward the edge

Materials for Lesson 2:

30 index cards from Lesson 1

Markers or colored pencils

(red, blue, brown, green, purple, orange)

Lesson 2

More
Grammar Power

Parts of Speech Chart

Determiner	Adjective	Noun	Verb	Adverb	Prepositional Phrase
The	squishy	worm	stretches	desperately	toward the edge

My worm sentence with an adverbial opener:

_____

_____

My favorite (silly) sentence with a prepositional opener:

_____

_____

Build a Sentence

Choose a noun (make it a proper noun!).

_____
noun

Use the same noun. Add an adjective.

_____   _____
adjoctive   noun

Use the same noun and adjective. Now add a verb.

_____   _____   _____
adjective   noun   verb

Next, add an adverb.

_____ _____ _____ _____
adjective   noun   verb   adverb

Continuing to use all the same words as above, add a prepositional phrase and a determiner (if needed).

____ _____ _____ _____ _____
(determiner) adjective   noun   verb   adverb

_____
prepositional phrase

Write your sentence below. Include a determiner if necessary. Add more powerful parts of speech and figurative language. You may choose to start with an adverbial or prepositional opener.

_____

_____

_____

15

It is a dog.

~~It is a dog.~~

Photo by Ron Fung, Unsplash

Try this pattern. Use **powerful** words.

(det.) adjective noun verb adverb prepositional phrase

_____

_____

_____

Lesson 3

Figurative Language

Simile

Compares two things using like or as

Her face was as red as a tomato.
Your smooth singing is like butter.

Metaphor

Compares two things without using like or as

Your bedroom is a disaster area.

Alliteration

A group of words that start with the same sound

My finicky feline feasts on fish.

Onomatopoeia

Sounds words

Whee! Pop! Bang! Shhhh! Hissss! Achoo! Meow.

Hyperbole

A big exaggeration

I'm so hungry I could eat the whole restaurant.
You run faster than a speeding bullet.

Personification

Gives human abilities to something that's not human.

The leaf danced across the road.
The sun told us it was time to go home.

That is a big cat. It is chasing a mouse.
~~That is a big cat. It is chasing a mouse.~~

Add one type of figurative language to the first sentence.

_____

_____

Add another type of figurative language to the second sentence.

_____

_____

Combine your sentences and add a *third* type of figurative language.

_____

_____

_____

_____

Rewrite your two sentences with the three types of figurative language and add in a few more descriptive nouns, adjectives, adverbs, and prepositional phrases.

_____

_____

_____

_____

_____

_____

Lesson 4

Manipulating the Reader

Five-senses Words

Sight
Sparkling, ruby-red, discolored, blurry, glowing, speckled, vivid, pale, vibrant, dim, striped, blackened, indigo

Sound
Thumping, squeaky, piercing, crispy, jangling, mooing, buzzing, silent, high-pitched, ringing, melodic, harmonious

Smell
Pungent, lemon-scented, perfumed, musty, stinky, aromatic, stench, flowery, putrid, odorous, fragrant,

Touch
Gritty, slimy, sticky, satiny-smooth, bumpy, fiery-hot, velvety, sharp, fiery-hot, chilled, gooey, moist, scratchy

Taste
Zesty, sweet, stale, tangy, succulent, flavorful, bitter, tart, acidic, rancid, spicy, bland, savory, bittersweet, delectable

My product: _____

5-senses words related to my product:

- Sight _____
- Sound _____
- Smell _____
- Touch _____
- Taste _____

My packaging: _____

_____

_____

_____

_____

_____

_____

_____

_____

_____

Optional drawing:

"Don't say the old lady screamed, bring her out and let her scream!"   - Mark Twain

Emotions	Body Language
Happy	Smiles Jumps Giggles Claps Slaps knee
Angry	Clenched teeth Fists Stomps Squinting Red-faced Growls
Nervous	Quivering Chews lip Big eyes Fidgets with shirt Heart pounding
Surprised	Mouth open Big eyes Inhale sharply Jump Scream Gasp
Scared	Hands over mouth Chews fingernails Shrieks Tears in eyes Whimpers Breathes quickly

_____
_____
_____
_____
_____
_____
_____
_____
_____
_____
_____
_____
_____
_____
_____
_____

Your "Super-novel" Passage

Decide the mood of your passage. Check one:

_____gloomy _____tense _____scary _____sad _____lonely
_____peaceful _____happy _____thrilling _____silly
_____ (other::_____)

What is the setting of this passage? (Check all that apply.)

_____outside _____indoors _____city _____country _____morning
_____afternoon _____evening _____night _____tropical
_____desert/dry _____northwoods _____beach _____mountains
_____Arctic/Antarctic _____plains _____(other::_____)

What is the weather? _____
(Is it a gentle snow or a blizzard? Is the sun warm or scorching? How do people react to this type of weather?)

If there are any people in your passage, how will you describe them?
(What would they wear? What kind of facial expressions do they have? What is their body language?)

_____
_____
_____
_____

Some tips:
Do not start with "It was…"
Start in the middle of the action.
Picture the scene in your mind and describe a couple details.

Sample paragraph:

Crash! Grandpa wiped his sweaty, furrowed brows as he crooned his neck in the direction of the unwelcome guest. Gingerly, he tip-toed toward the tool shed, the blaring sunshine bouncing off the silvery roof and nearly blinding him. He would stalk this belligerent varmint until it scampered out, then blast it to smithereens! Like a prowling cat ready to pounce, Grandpa waited, eager to meet his foe.

Super-novel Passage: A Rubric

I have included (check *at least two* in each section):

Powerful grammar words
Prepositional phrase _____
Adverbial opener _____
Strong adjectives and verbs _____

Figurative language
Simile _____
Metaphor _____
Alliteration _____
Hyperbole _____
Personification _____
Onomatopoeia _____

Descriptive language
Weather words _____
Color words _____
Five senses words _____

Once you've included at least two features from each section, type your passage, proofread it, and print it. Include your name and date and give it a title.

28

Lesson 5

Organize Your Thoughts

From Junk Drawer to… Umbrella?!

Magic Eraser

Power 1_____

    Power 2_____

    Power 2_____

    Power 2_____

A **P1** is *always* the _____.

A **P2** is *always* the _____.

Practice

P1 states
    P2_____
    P2 Texas

P1_____
    P2 red
    P2 blue

P1 _____
    P2 arm
    P2 leg

P1 furniture
    P2 chair
    P2_____

P1 family members
    P2_____
    P2_____

P1 books
    P2 Old Yeller
    P2 _____

P1 trees
    P2 maple
    P2 oak

P1 sports
    P2 basketball
    P2 fun

P1 restaurants
    P2 french fries
    P2 McDonald's

P1 cartoon characters
    P2 Mickey Mouse
    P2 Bugs Bunny

P1 candy
    P2 suckers
    P2 sticky

P1 house pets
    P2 cats
    P2 elephants

Practice

P1 trees   P1_____

    P2 pine   P2_____

    P2 maple   P2_____

    P2 oak   P2_____

P1_____   P1_____

    P2_____   P2_____

    P2_____   P2_____

    P2_____   P2_____

P1_____   P1_____

    P2_____   P2_____

    P2_____   P2_____

    P2_____   P2_____

P1_____   P1_____

    P2_____   P2_____

    P2_____   P2_____

    P2_____   P2_____

*Remember, a P1 is *always* the _____.

P1 pasta
    P2 macaroni
    P2 shell
    P2 bowtie
P1_____

Transition Words for P2s

First, Second, Third,
To begin, Next, Last,
One (way), In addition, Finally,
First, Next, Finally,

Terminal Signals for P1 Closings

In conclusion,
To conclude,
In sum,
As you can see,
In short,

My Written Paragraph:

_____

_____

_____

_____

_____

_____

_____

_____

Lesson 6

Power Paragraphs

More Powerful Pasta Paragraph

P1 pasta

    P2 macaroni

    P2 shell

    P2 bowtie

P1 pasta

P0 _____

P1 pasta

    P2 macaroni

    P2 shell

    P2 bowtie

P1 pasta

P0 _____

A P0 opening _____.

A P0 closing _____.

Outline to Paragraph with Power 0s

    Mama mia! It's an Italian feast! I have three kinds of pasta in my bowl. First, I have macaroni pasta. Next, I have shell pasta. Finally, I have bowtie pasta. As you can see, my bowl is loaded with several kinds of pasta. What's in your bowl?

Paragraphs Matter

Photo by Rawpixel, Unsplash

P0 _____

P1 There are 3 forms of matter.

       P2 _____

       P2 _____

       P2 _____

P1 _____

P0 _____

P0 "Attention-Getters"

- Matter matters!
- Matter is defined as "anything that has mass and takes up space."
- Did you know that H_2O can be ice, water, or steam?

P0 "Leave the Reader Thinking"

- Take a nature walk sometime. Can you identify three forms of matter on your walk?
- Next time you drink an icy glass of water on a steamy day, consider how much matter matters!
- Can you name forms of matter found in your fridge? It might be fun (and tasty) to try!

Your Own Outline

P0_____

 P1_____

      P2 _____

      P2 _____

      P2 _____

P1_____

P0_____

Your Outline as a Paragraph

(Be sure to include a number word, a transition, or a terminal signal for each sentence.)

_____

_____

_____

_____

_____

_____

_____

_____

_____

_____

_____

_____

_____

Lesson 7

Details, Details

Tell Me More

P0 Attention-getter (hook)

P1 Subject

    P2 Example

        P3 _____

    P2 Example

        P3 _____

    P2 Example

        P3 _____

P1 Subject

P0 Leave the reader thinking

P0 Stomach growling

P1 3 favorite snacks

    P2 popcorn

        P3 lots of butter

    P2 _____

        P3 _____

    P2 _____

        P3 _____

P1 Favorite snacks

P0 Tame the tummy

Speak the above completed outline as a paragraph using complete sentences.

Try This…

Now that you've spoken the "favorite snacks" paragraph, try writing it here.

_____

_____

_____

_____

_____

_____

_____

_____

_____

_____

_____

Photo by Georgia Vagim, Unsplash

41

Practice

Write a paragraph with the following P1.

I want to win $100 for three reasons.

Include an outline that has Power 0s, Power 1s, three P2s, and P3s for each P2. (Remember not to use complete sentences.)

Speak your paragraph from your outline first, then write it. (Make it as silly and fun as you dare!)

Create your power outline on this page and write your paragraph on the next page.

My Outline

My Paragraph

_____

_____

_____

_____

_____

_____

_____

_____

_____

_____

_____

_____

_____

_____

_____

_____

_____

_____

_____

Writing an Essay: The Magic Formula

P0: attention-getter ("hook")
P1: subject (thesis)

P2: example of the subject
    P3: detail about the example
        P4: detail about that detail
    P3: detail about the example
        P4: detail about that detail

P2: example of the subject
    P3: detail about the example
        P4: detail about that detail
    P3: detail about the example
        P4: detail about that detail

P2: example of the subject
    P3: detail about the example
        P4: detail about that detail
    P3: detail about the example
        P4: detail about that detail

P1: subject (thesis)
P0: leave the reader thinking

* Remember to plug in a number word for your P1 opening (tells how many P2s), transition words for every P2 sentence, and a terminal signal for your P1 closing.

Writing a Four-Paragraph Essay

Step One: Select your P1 subject. (Circle one.)

I have two favorite books.

I play two sports.

I have experienced two favorite vacations.

I have two favorite video games.

I have two awesome hobbies.

I have two sisters/brothers/siblings.

Step Two: List your P2 examples here.

P2_____

P2_____

Step Three: Fill out a graphic organizer or make a Power Outline.
(See next two pages.)

Step Four: Write it or type it in sentences.
Use transition words and terminal signals. Add more powerful words, an adverbial or prepositional opener, figurative language, and five-senses words.

Graphic Organizer: Four-paragraph Essay

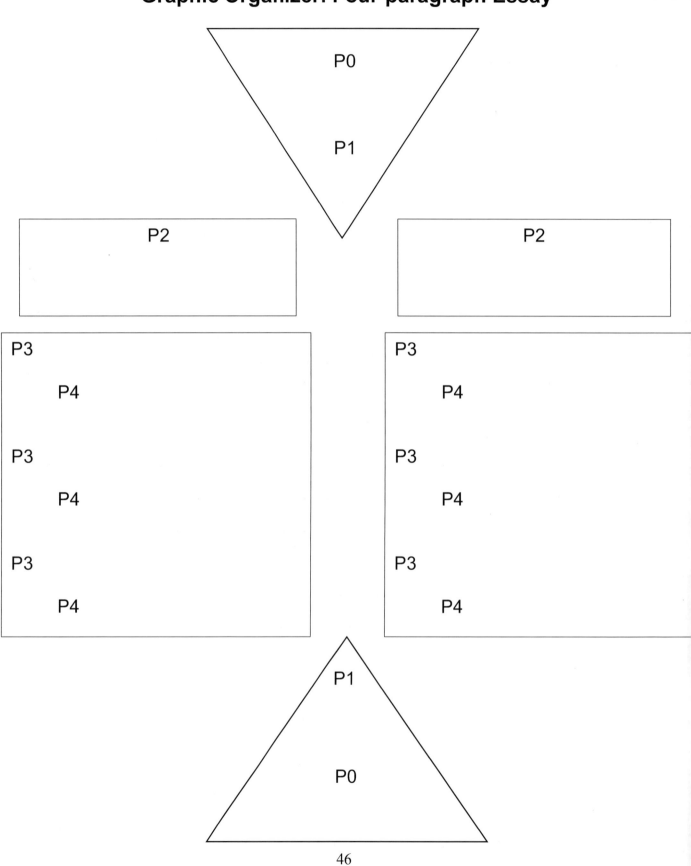

Power Outline: Four-Paragraph Essay

P0 _____

P1 _____

    P2 _____

        P3 _____

            P4 _____

        P3 _____

            P4 _____

        P3 _____

            P4 _____

    P2 _____

        P3 _____

            P4 _____

        P3 _____

            P4 _____

        P3 _____

            P4 _____

P1 _____

P0 _____

When typing (or writing) your essay, remember:

1. Each line of your outline (or graphic organizer) gets its own sentence.
2. Use a number word for your first P1, transition words for each P2, and a terminal signal for your P1 closing.
3. Incorporate powerful grammar, figurative language, and descriptive writing.
4. Include your name and date on your essay, as well as a title.
5. Before you print your essay, check for spelling and punctuation.

Essay Checklist

Key Components	Done
I used the power-writing formula (P0s, P1s, P2s, P3s, and P4s).	
I indented the first sentence of each new paragraph.	
I included transition words in my P2s.	
I included a terminal signal in my P1 closing.	
I used specific nouns.	
I used powerful verbs.	
I used at least 5 powerful adjectives.	
I used at least 3 powerful adverbs.	
I included prepositional phrases.	
I included at least one prepositional or adverbial opener.	
I incorporated figurative language at least once.	
I used five-senses words.	
I checked my spelling.	
I checked my punctuation.	

Lesson 8

The Motherload

Review the Formula

P0 attention-getter

P1_____ (use a number word in your essay)

    P2_____ (use a transition word in your essay)

        P3 detail about the example

           P4_____

        P3_____

           P4_____

P2 example of the subject

        P3_____

           P4_____

        P3_____

           P4_____

    P2_____

        P3_____

           P4_____

        P3_____

        P4 detail about the detail

P1 subject (use a transition word in your essay)

P0_____

Sample Power Outline
Title: Matter Matters

(First Paragraph)
P0: Matter matters!
P1: 3 forms of matter

(Second Paragraph)
    P2: solids
        P3: molecules close together
            P4: don't move
        P3: doesn't bend easily (conform)
            P4: keeps shape in containers
        P3: often becomes liquid if heated
            P4: ice to water

(Third Paragraph)
    P2: liquids
        P3: molecules farther apart
            P4: move
        P3: takes shape of container (conforms)
            P4: tall, skinny glass vs. short, fat glass
        P3: often becomes gas if heated
            P4: water to steam

(Fourth Paragraph)
    P2: gases
        P3: molecules very far apart
            P4: move & spread out
        P3: takes shape of container
            P4: balloons
        P3: often becomes liquid if cooled
            P4: cloud to rain

(Fifth Paragraph)
P1 Closing: 3 forms of matter
P0: Take a walk, identify ...

Matter Matters

Matter matters! The popular "Webster's Dictionary" defines matter as anything that takes up space and has mass. Everything on our enormous earth is some form of matter. In fact, matter can be found in one of three forms: solids, liquids, and gases.

Solids constitute one form of matter. There are three common characteristics of a solid. For example, the molecules in solids are stubborn! They are densely packed, which means they can't move easily. Another characteristic of solids is that they don't conform. If you were to put a wooden block into a plastic baggie, it would not change its shape. A final characteristic of solids is that they often become liquid when they are heated. When ice is warmed, it becomes liquid water.

Liquids are a second form of matter. One property of liquids is that their molecules are farther apart than solid molecules. That means the molecules are able to move a little easier too. Also, unlike solids, liquids do take the shape of their container (conform). For example, water takes the shape of whatever glass it is in, whether it is tall and skinny or short and wide. And finally, when liquid is heated it usually turns into a gas. The molecules in water start to move faster and spread apart when it is heated, causing it to turn into steam.

That brings us to the third form of matter: gases. Molecules in a gas are very far apart—especially compared to solids! They dance around and spread out as much as possible. Gases also take the shape of their container. If you've ever blown up a birthday balloon, you've witnessed a gas (the carbon dioxide you're exhaling) take the shape of the balloon. A final property of a gas is that when it becomes cooled it often turns into a liquid. For example, a cloud consists of water in the form of a gas that condenses and forms water droplets that fall to earth as rain.

In summary, there are three forms of matter: solids, liquids, and gases. Each of these amazing forms of matter are found throughout the earth and have unique characteristics. Take a walk sometime and see if you can identify the three forms throughout nature. You'll find that matter really does matter!

Bibliography

Frank, Marjorie Slavick. *Harcourt Science*, Orlando, FL, Harcourt School Publishers, 2000.

What is a Bibliography?

A bibliography is an alphabetical list of all the print and nonprint sources that were used to find information for a writing project. These sources can include books, encyclopedias, magazine articles, websites, newspaper articles, pamphlets, interviews, and so on. The bibliography is usually a separate page or section place at the end of the report.

Patterns and Examples of How to Format a Bibliography

Book Format
Author's last name, first name, and middle initial. *Title of book.* Place of publication: Publishing company, year of publication. Print.

Book Example
Lewis, Clive.S. *The Chronicles of Narnia: The Lion, the Witch, and the Wardrobe.* New York: Harper Collins Publishers. 1950. Print.

Magazine Format
Author's last name, first name, and middle initial. "Article Title." *Title of Magazine.* Date Month Year Published: Page(s). Print.

Magazine Example
Flowers, Laura T. "Bicycling for Fitness." *Bicycling Times.* December 2005: 13-16. Print.

Website Format
Author's last name, first name, and middle initial. "Title of article/document." *Title of site.* Name of editor if available (first and last name, if available). Date of most recent update. Name of organization associated with site. Date when you accessed the document. Web.

Website Example
Brookins, Amanda. "Starting a Home-based Business as a Teen." *ehow Money.* 2012. Demand Media. July 10, 2012. Web.

*Note: Websites do not always provide the author's name and/or the editor's name. In that case, the title of the article is first.

Power Outline for Your Academic Five-Paragraph Essay

(You can decide how many P3s and P4s per P2.)

P0_____

P1_____

    P2_____

      P3_____

        P4_____

      P3_____

        P4_____

    P2_____

      P3_____

        P4_____

      P3_____

        P4_____

    P2_____

      P3_____

        P4_____

      P3_____

        P4_____

P1_____

P0_____

Essay Checklist

Key Components	Done
I used the power-writing formula (P0s, P1s, P2s, P3s, and P4s).	
I indented the first sentence of each new paragraph.	
I included transition words in my P2s.	
I included a terminal signal in my P1 closing.	
I used specific nouns.	
I used powerful verbs.	
I used at least 5 powerful adjectives.	
I used at least 3 powerful adverbs.	
I included prepositional phrases.	
I included at least one prepositional or adverbial opener.	
I incorporated figurative language at least once.	
I used five-senses words.	
I checked my spelling.	
I checked my punctuation.	
I included a bibliography.	

Let's Review!

Write a sentence about this picture. Include a determiner, an adjective, a noun, a verb, an adverb, and a prepositional phrase. Use powerful words!

Photo by Nathan Anderson, Unsplash

_____

_____

_____

Improve the sentence below three times. Each time, use a different kind of figurative language.

The bullfrog jumped onto a lily pad and croaked.

1._____

_____

2._____

_____

3._____

_____

Write a paragraph about a brother and sister who are terrified of a thunderstorm they're experiencing. Avoid using the words "afraid," "scared," "terrified," or anything resembling them. Do use five-senses words and body language. Start in the middle of the action and describe just one scene.

_____

_____

_____

_____

_____

_____

_____

_____

_____

_____

_____

_____

_____

_____

_____

_____

Write two powerful words that you can use to replace "big."

_____   _____

Write a more powerful way to describe something that is red.

_____

Write two more powerful words you can use to replace "said."

_____   _____

Label the umbrella below.
Use words about ice cream flavors.

Use the umbrella words to
create a power outline below.

In the space below, create your "Ice Cream" **outline with P0s and P3s** added.

_____

_____

_____

_____

_____

_____

_____

_____

Write a paragraph from your ice cream outline. Be sure to include a number word, transition words, and a terminal signal.

_____

_____

_____

_____

_____

_____

_____

_____

_____

_____

_____

_____

Photo by Mark Cruz, Unsplash

Answer Keys

Answer Key

Lesson 1: Grammar Power (pages 10-11)

Noun Examples

(See list of nouns. Answers will vary.) Nouns name a person, place, thing, or idea.

Adjective Examples

(See list of adjectives. Answers will vary.) Adjectives describe nouns.

Verb Examples

(See list of verbs. Answers will vary.) Verbs are action words and words of being or having.

Adverb Examples

(See list of adverbs. Answers will vary.) Adverbs are words that describe verbs (*how* something happens or *when* it happens).

Determiner Examples

For his exercise, use "a," "an," or "the," which are all articles in the broader category of "determiners."

Prepositional Phrase Examples

(See list of prepositions and prepositional phrases. Answers will vary.) Prepositions are often words of position. The student's examples should be at least two words.

Lesson 2: More Grammar Power

Part A

The chart (page 14) is color-coordinated. For example, students wrote nouns in red, so the "Noun" column will have the words that were written in red on their index cards. That column will have words that represent a person, place, thing, or idea.

My worm sentence with an adverbial opener:

Desperately the squishy worm stretches toward the edge.

My favorite silly sentence with a prepositional opener:

(Example) Toward the edge the squishy worm stretches desperately.

Part B

Build a Sentence (page 15)

Students should use the same noun, adjective, verb, adverb, and prepositional phrase throughout the exercise.

Example final sentence: At midnight the exhausted Sam plopped heavily into his bed.

It is a dog. (page 16)

Example final sentence: The joyful canine pounced eagerly onto his shadow.

Lesson 3: Figurative Language
Part B
That is a big cat. It is chasing a mouse. **(page 19)**
Example of adding one type of figurative language to the first sentence:
That cat is as big as the moon.
Example of adding another type to the second sentence:
It is chasing a marvelous microscopic mouse.
Example of combining the sentences and adding a third type of figurative language:
That cat is as big as the moon. It is chasing a marvelous microscopic mouse. Splat!
Example of rewriting with more powerful and descriptive language:
That calico feline is as gigantic as the moon. It surges furiously toward a marvelous microscopic mouse. Splat!

Lesson 4: Manipulating the Reader
Part A
(page 23) Example of a Sample Product: mechanical pencil
Example of Five-senses Words Related to My Product:
Sight – vibrant, glowing, shiny, golden brown
Sound – crisp, scratch-scratch
Smell – home-baked cookies
Touch – Smooth, fluid
Taste – mouth-watering, minty, sweet, chocolatey, chewy
Example of My Packaging: If you've been frustrated with your old #2, feast your eyes upon this deluxe mechanical pencil! The smooth scritch-scratching of the chocolatey-brown lead is so sweet it will conjure up memories of your grandma's home-baked cookies fresh from the oven and have your page filled with the chewy, delicious words you've been longing to savor for so long. Gone are the days of writer's block! Once you've tasted the success this golden mechanical pencil can produce, you'll never go back. Take one home today!
Part B
(page 25) Example of Two Angry Cowboys: Horace took a moment to regroup, stranding tall as his lips curled and his eyes pierced menacingly at his foe. Raising his clenched fist into the air as a distraction, he slid his other hand slowly into his holster while the sweat beaded on his forehead and his jaw tightened. His resolve to avenge the loss of his pride was as sure as the heat of the noonday sun which now beat mercilessly on both men.

Part C

Super-novel Passage (typed on own paper, based on pages 26-27)

This assignment is meant to be a demonstration of the student's ability to employ all the writing features presented thus far. Read your student's paragraph and compare it with the rubric. The student should have included two features from each section of the rubric. If possible, the paragraph should be typed with a name and date and have a centered title.

Lesson 5: Organize Your Thoughts
Part A
From Junk Drawer to… Umbrella?! (page 30)

Each umbrella should have a group name in the top, with three examples in the group on the three lines.

Example: if the group name is batteries, the three lines could include A, AA, AAA.

Another example: If Legos is the group name, the three lines could include yellow, red, and blue.

Magic Eraser (page 31) Students draw the umbrella, fill it in, then erase the umbrella to discover they've created an outline.

Power 1 Subject
> Power 2 Example
> Power 2 Example
> Power 2 Example

A P1 is always the *subject*.

A P2 is always the *example*.

Practice (page 32)

P1 states
> P2 (*students write any state here, such as Wisconsin*)
> P2 Texas

P1 *colors*
> P2 red
> P2 blue

P1 *body parts* (or limbs, etc)
> P2 arm
> P2 leg

P1 furniture
> P2 chair
> P2 *table* (or other furniture examples)

P1 family members
> P2 (words like brother, uncle, etc. or specific names of personal family members)
> P2 (words like brother, uncle, etc. or specific names of personal family members)

P1 books
    P2 Old Yeller
    P2 *Charlotte's Web* (or a title of any other book)
P1 trees: thumbs up, no changes
P1 sports: thumbs down, "fun" is not an example, replace with baseball or other sport
P1 restaurants: thumbs down, French fries are not an example of restaurants. Replace with Waffle House or other restaurant example.
P1 cartoon characters: thumbs up, no changes
P1 candy: thumbs down, "sticky" is not an example, replace with candy bar or other example.
P1 house pets: thumbs down, "elephants" are not house pets, replace with dogs or other appropriate example.

Part B

Practice (page 33): Students should complete each outline so the P1 is the subject and each P1 has three examples under it.

(Page 34) *Remember, a P1 is always the <u>subject</u>.

P1 pasta
    P2 macaroni
    P2 shell
    P2 bowtie
P1 *pasta*

Example of "My Written Paragraph": I have three kinds of pasta in my bowl. First, I have macaroni pasta. Second, I have shell pasta. Third, I have bowtie pasta. As you can see, I have several kinds of pasta in my bowl. (Students should have each line of their outline represented as a full sentence.)

Lesson 6: Power Paragraphs

Part A

More Powerful Pasta Paragraph (page 36)

P0 *Mama Mia! Feast…*
P0 *Your bowl?*

Part B

Paragraphs Matter (page 37)

One example:
    P0 *Matter Matters!*
    P1 3 forms of matter.
        P2 *solids*
        P2 *liquids*
        P2 *gases*
    P1 *3 forms*

P0 *Nature walk… identify 3 forms?*
Another example:
P0 *Matter is defined as…*
P1 3 forms of matter
P2 *solids*
P2 *liquids*
P2 *gases*
P1 *3 forms*
P0 *Next time you drink…*

Your Own Outline (page 38)
Sample outline:
P0 "ruff" day?
P1 3 dog breeds
P2 collie
P2 golden retriever
P2 beagle
P1 dog breeds
P0 happy to be with
Your Outline as a Paragraph
Sample paragraph: Having a "ruff" day? A canine companion could be the answer. I know about three kinds of dog breeds. One dog breed I know about is the collie. Another kind of dog breed I know about is the golden retriever. Finally, I know about the beagle. In sum, I know several kinds of dog breeds. They're always happy to be with their owners. If you own one, you know what I mean!

Lesson 7: Details, Details
Part A
Tell Me More (page 40)
(Top half of page)
P3 Detail
P3 Detail
P3 Detail
(Bottom half of page)
P0 Stomach growling
P1 3 fave snacks
P2 popcorn
P3 lots of butter
P2 *apple* (or other snack example)
P3 *with peanut butter* (student should provide detail of his snack in P2)

P2 *trail mix* (or other snack example)

      P3 nuts, dried apples, chocolate chips (student should provide a detail of her snack in P2)

P1 Fave snacks

P0 Tame the tummy

Students should *speak* this outline as a paragraph and use a number word for their P1 opening, transition words for their P2s, and a terminal signal for their P1 closing.

Try This… (page 41)

Sample written paragraph about snacks:

By three o'clock in the afternoon, my stomach is growling like a threatening lion. I have three favorite snacks. One snack I enjoy crunching is popcorn. I especially love it with lots of butter drizzled over the top. Another snack that really satisfies is a crisp, juicy apple. I like to dip it into creamy peanut butter for a special treat. Finally, I like to snack on trail mix. My favorite trail mix includes mixed nuts, dried apples, and chocolate chips. As you can see, I have several favorite snacks. Next time my stomach begins to roar, I know what to do so I can easily tame my tummy!

Practice (page 42)

Student outlines will look like this:

P0

P1

  P2

      P3

  P2

      P3

  P2

      P3

P1

P0

Outlines will be filled in with their ideas (can be silly!) and may have more than one P3 per P2.

My Paragraph (page 43)

Example of a paragraph about winning $100:

One Hundred Bucks Might as Well Be a Million

There's a hundred-dollar greenback up for grabs, and the entire world depends on me winning it! I long to win that $100 for three completely rational reasons. One reason I yearn for that crisp money is that I'll be faithfully investing a portion of it into my elusive college fund. When I graduate from college, I'll be equipped to travel the world and promote peace and justice. Another reason that $100 will come in handy is to fork over my share of an exclusive dinner with the president. Imagine the impact of me having his ear for a couple hours! Finally, I'd like to win that cold, hard cash so I can buy vegetable seeds and plant organic crops in my back yard. I could harvest the fresh vegetables faster than a speeding bullet and immediately donate them to the needy! As you can see, that $100 would go to good use if I won it! Between striving for world peace, waxing eloquent at a dinner with the president, and donating my high-quality garden produce, it's evident that $100 would multiply into a million!

Part B

Writing a Four-Paragraph Essay (page 45)

Step One: Students circle one option.

Step Two: List your P2 examples here.

P2 (student lists an example from the chosen P1 subject)

P2 (student lists another example from the same chosen P1 subject)

Power Outline: Four-Paragraph Essay (page 47)

Example of an outline:

P0 bucket list

P1 2 fave vacations

     P2 Europe

          P3 Paris, France

               P4 Eiffel Tower, Louvre Museum, Notre Dame Cathedral

          P3 Italy

               P4 Rome, Pompeii, Island of Capri

          P3 Germany

               P4 Bavarian Alps, Neuschwanstein Castle

     P2 Canada

          P3 Banff camping near the lake

               P4 Hiked Fairview Mountain overlooking Lake Louise

          P3 Jasper

               P4 Swam in pool fed by natural hot springs

          P3 Calgary

               P4 Toured city, out to eat

P1 fave vacations

P0 more items on bucket list

When typing essay, remember:

Students will complete their four-paragraph essays by creating a sentence out of each line item in their outline (or graphic organizer). Finished essays should be typed and students should have marked each key component on their checklist **(page 48).**

Lesson 8: The Motherload

Part A

Review the Formula (page 50)

P0 attention-getter

P1 *subject*

P2 *example of the subject*
  P3 detail about the example
    P4 *detail about the detail*
  P3 *detail about the example*
    P4 *detail about the detail*
P2 example of the subject
  P3 *detail about the example*
    P4 *detail about the detail*
  P3 *detail about the example*
    P4 *detail about the detail*
P2 *example of the subject*
  P3 *detail about the example*
    P4 *detail about the detail*
  P3 *detail about the example*
    P4 *detail about the detail*

P1 subject

P0 *leave reader thinking*

Power Outline for Your Academic Five-Paragraph Essay (page 55)

Students choose a topic they've already studied (or are currently studying) for school. They can choose number of P3s and P4s for each section. Once the outline is complete, they should type their essay and include a Bibliography. They should be able to mark every line on their checklist **(page 56).**

Part B

Let's Review

(Page 58) Sample sentence: The amused fox howls excitedly at his companions. Improve the sentence below three times.

Sample:

1. The bullfrog jumped a mile onto a lily pad and croaked.
2. The bullfrog that's as big as a pumpkin jumped a mile onto a lily pad and croaked.
3. The bullfrog that's as big as a pumpkin jumped a mile onto a lily pad. "Crooooak!"

Short paragraph (page 59)

Sample paragraph:

  Maria nose-dived into her brother's bed and gripped him as though he were a life preserver that had been flung to her amidst a storm-tossed sea. He jolted awake just as the next thunderous roar rattled the windows of his usually peaceful bedroom. Peering from beneath his covers, his eyes widened as he realized why she was there. He mirrored her expression. With his lips quivering and eyebrows furrowed he grasped her trembling hand. At that instant, the room filled with a blinding light and crashing thunder as the two scurried hand-in-hand toward the safety of their parents' room.

(Page 60) Two words to replace "big" (examples = humungous, gigantic…)
More powerful way to replace "red" (examples = candy-apple red, rose-colored…)
More powerful words to replace "said" (examples = exclaimed, hollered, questioned…)
Label the umbrella with words about ice cream flavors. (Examples = "ice cream flavors" in the top and "strawberry," "chocolate," and "vanilla" on the lines.)
Power outline for the above example:
P1 ice cream flavors
     P2 strawberry
     P2 chocolate
     P2 vanilla
P1 ice cream flavors
(Page 61) Add P0s and P3s to the outline.
Sample:
P0 cold snack, hot day
P1 ice cream flavors
     P2 strawberry
          P3 chunks of big red berries
     P2 chocolate
          P3 on a waffle cone
     P2 vanilla
          P3 add caramel topping
P1 ice cream flavors
P0 craving it now
Write a paragraph from the ice cream outline. (page 62)
Sample:

    There's nothing better than a cold snack on a hot day – especially when it's ice cream! I have three favorite ice cream flavors. My first favorite flavor is strawberry. I love the gigantic chunks of berry goodness spread throughout. My second favorite ice cream flavor is chocolate. Scoop it onto a chocolate-dipped waffle cone and I'm one happy camper. My third favorite flavor is vanilla. The ultimate serving of vanilla ice cream has caramel sauce drizzled luxuriously over the top with a light smattering of pecans. As you can see, I have some delightfully delicious favorite ice cream flavors. It makes my mouth water just thinking about them!

Made in the USA
Columbia, SC
20 March 2019

Writing for Grades 4-8

Watch your student transform into an encouraged, organized, and equipped writer!

Thorough.

Students will:

- Create vivid word pictures with figurative language.
- "Manipulate" the reader using five-senses words.
- Employ more effective communication skills using powerful grammar and syntax.
- Author highly descriptive paragraphs using a writing technique taught by Mark Twain.
- Transfer information from their head to the paper by organizing their thinking.
- Memorize a simple, numeric formula for crafting informative paragraphs and essays.
- Compose a four-paragraph essay on a subject in which they are the expert.
- Compose a five-paragraph academic essay that includes a bibliography.

Simple.

Students will:

- Think without thinking they're thinking!
- Receive straightforward, direct instruction in a simple setting.
- Copy words for ease of spelling and maintaining momentum.
- Create color-coded index cards to play with syntax and parts of speech.
- Master one concept before moving on to the next.
- Move from single words to phrases to sentences to paragraphs to essays.
- Implement an easy formula to produce well-organized essays.
- Visualize the organization of a basic essay with a graphic organizer.

Engaging.

Students will:

- Be inspired by worms and watch the instructor dare to eat one.
- Create hysterical sentences from powerful parts of speech.
- Discover figurative language with balloon-popping and noise-making
- Advertise a product with highly motivating language.
- Describe a volatile scene from the old west.
- Become a "world-famous novelist."
- Compare a junk drawer to their thoughts and learn how to organize both.
- Craft a creative and well-structured paragraph that explains what zany activities they would do with $100.

"We had fabulous success with the writing class! My son now wants to enter an essay contest... whereas a year ago that was punishment for him to hear about the idea of writing an essay!" -Sarah S.

This workbook accompanies the video teachings available at PowerHouseEdu.com.

POWERHOUSE
educational resources

ISBN 9781733699808

9 781733 699808